The All Night Bookshop

ex libris

Candlestick Press

Published by:
Candlestick Press,
Diversity House, 72 Nottingham Road, Arnold, Nottingham UK NG5 6LF
www.candlestickpress.co.uk

Design and typesetting by Diversity Creative Marketing Solutions Ltd.,
www.diversity.agency

Printed by Ratcliff & Roper Print Group, Nottinghamshire, UK

ISBN 978 1 907598 76 0

Acknowledgements:

The text and poems in this pamphlet are reprinted from the following
books, all by permission of the publishers listed unless stated otherwise.
Every effort has been made to trace the copyright holders; however, the
editor and publisher apologise if any material has been included without
permission or without appropriate acknowledgement, and would be glad
to be told of anyone who has not been consulted. Thanks are due to all
the copyright holders cited below for their kind permission:

Jim Burns, *let's do it: late poems* (The Black Light Engine Room Press,
2018) reprinted by kind permission of the author.

Jackie Kay, first appeared in *Off the Shelf: A Celebration of Bookshops in
Verse*, ed. Carol Ann Duffy (Picador 2016), reprinted by kind permission
of the author.

Bookshops

It's difficult to find one these days,
a dusty place piled high with books,
and looked after by an old man
sitting in a corner by an electric fire.
The rest of the shop cold and draughty.
"There could be something upstairs,"
he'd say, in answer to a question,
"or try the small back room,
but be careful, and watch out for the cat."
There was always a cat.
And up the rickety stairs,
or in that back room full of boxes,
you might find something
it was worth getting grubby hands for,
and dust on the knees of your trousers.
An old magazine, a slim volume of poetry,
a novel that no-one remembers anymore.
You could buy them for almost nothing.
"It's easier on the Internet," someone says.
"But not as much fun," I reply.

Jim Burns

The All Night Bookshop

The All Night Bookshop is easy to miss. Its windows are dusty and display-free. There's no sign, nor a notice of opening hours. During the day, it looks like many other premises in the old part of the city centre: closed due to declining demand, awaiting redevelopment. Only The All Night Bookshop's customers know that we open every night, except Sunday, sometime between ten and eleven. I don't know how it happens they first find us, yet find us they do.

Most nights, I arrive at work around ten. Before opening up, I check the answering machine (the store isn't connected to the internet, but our landline works). Then I go through the post and process any orders. Zelda handles periodicals. I watch her artfully display the magazines and newspapers, putting aside those reserved for individual customers.

The shop sells books of every size, shape and category. Customers often say that ours is the best-stocked bookshop in the city. There are three floors – five if you include a basement used for storage and an attic flat where the owner lives. Neither Zelda nor I have ever met the owner. Nor do we know his or her name.

I've worked here for just over a year. Zelda hired me after I wandered in one sleepless evening. Instantly smitten, I wanted to chat her up, so asked about the position vacant sign on the counter. She gave me a trial and took me on the following morning.

Many of our customers are insomniacs. We do get a certain 'normal' clientele during our first hour: bus drivers coming off duty, people popping in after a visit to a theatre, cinema or pub. But we discourage them with the irregularity of our opening time. The real customers start to arrive well after midnight. Many live in the city and come by foot. Others drive here and park nearby. They ignore the restrictions outside, for no traffic wardens work such unsocial hours. Taxis come and go. Our floors are seldom empty.

Some customers phone first to see whether we have a particular book in stock. People have been known to travel a hundred miles wearing just slippers and a dressing gown. The urge to own a book can be a particularly powerful one, and the intensity of those phone calls is a testament to the importance of the service we provide.

The availability of stock on the internet does not appear to have affected our trade. Printed books cannot be delivered in the middle of the night, after all. Moreover, some of our customers express distaste for the new-fangled "electronic" books that can be downloaded instantly. I have no problem with them, though I do find that the information I absorb from a screen does not sink in quite so deeply as that derived from the printed page.

"Best sellers" we leave to the mainstream bookshops, supermarkets and Amazon. We are not in competition with anyone. The bookshop's turnover is so slow that much of our stock is old and otherwise out of print. Luckily, our customers like this aspect. They say they find surprises on every shelf.

After a few weeks, Zelda put me in charge of orders. I take this role very seriously. During my early days at the shop I kept a record of which books had a spike in demand at particular times of the night. My results were as follows:

10-11pm   Mysteries. Rock Music. Car Manuals.
11-12pm   Celebrity Biographies. Sport. Russian Literature.
12-1am   Gardening. Chinese Architecture. Ornithology.
1-2am   World History. Icelandic Myths. Deep Sea Diving.
2-3am   Calligraphy. Erotica. Poetry.
3-4am   Inner Being. Witchcraft. Board Games.
4-5am   Diet Guides. Start Your Own Business. Cookery.
5-6am   Home Repairs. Children's. Meditation.
6-7am   Travel. Military. Graphic Novels.
7-7.30am   Dream Interpretation. Wind-chimes. Pottery.

Zelda is twenty-one, eighteen months my senior. Like me, she's a student. She started working at the bookshop a year before I did, two summers ago. She has never told me what course she does, or which of the city's two universities she studies at.

Zelda is very good at brushing away questions, so I soon learned to stop asking them. She will tell me what she wants me to find out. One day, for instance, she revealed that, like me, she has little to do with her family. Another time, she confided that she only needs three hours sleep a day, all of which she takes in catnaps. Maybe she sneaks sleep when she's behind the magazine counter. I have no way of knowing. I do know that she's blind in one eye, but I can never remember which, as her face is usually hidden by fine, straight hair, the colour of night.

As for me, I require a lot of sleep. Sometimes, in my tiny flat, I sleep so long that I'm late for work the following night. Asleep or awake, I dream a lot. Often, I dream of Zelda, who I am in love with, but hold out no hope of winning. I've never told Zelda this, but I dropped out of university at the end of my first year. I have no prospects beyond this shop.

I am not the only person obsessed by my co-worker. All night, I observe her insomniac admirers cruising the magazine section. She never encourages them, and this encourages me. I'm content to watch my love at work and be paid to do so. The pay is barely minimum wage, but we have a low turnover and lose a lot of stock to shoplifters, so the profits must be tiny. I often wonder how the owner keeps us going.

There are many stories concerning the nature of our owner. The most common is about a woman who ran the business with her husband. When he died she chose to open only during the hours of darkness. The bookshop, therefore, became a kind of shrine.

Another story concerns a rich, eccentric insomniac who often needs to find a book in the middle of the night. The insomniac disguises him or herself as a customer. Zelda and I sometimes play a game in which we speculate about which customer is really the owner. That one, with the length of string instead of a tie? Or the other, who resembles an eccentric professor and orders obscure Eastern European journals?

Or the middle-aged woman who buys three romantic novels at a time and insists that we accept the ones she's read in part exchange, even though we don't have a second-hand section?

In summer, as our night ends, some daylight seeps in from outside. This morning I pull down the shutters at seven and prepare to shut up shop. I nod at Zelda and begin my patrol of the bookshop's three floors, making sure that every customer has left. Occasionally I have to wake a sleeper who has chosen a quiet section in which to lie down between the bookcases. Not today. On the third floor, I always listen carefully for signs of the owner in the flat above, but have never heard a thing. Today is no different.

Zelda stands by the front door in a long, grey coat. This is unusual, for she always leaves after me. Once, I waited down the road, intending to follow her home. I wanted to know where she lived. But she must have realized what I was up to. That night, she didn't leave the shop at all. I hung around in the canopy of a closed-down music store, then waited until the street was busy with people on their way to work before, frustrated, I gave up. That night, Zelda seemed to look at me strangely, more distantly. I never tried to follow her again.

Before I have a chance to comment on the coat, Zelda speaks to me in her soft, matter-of-fact voice.

"I'm leaving the city today. I've graduated. You can take over if you want. Hire someone else, the way I hired you."

I'm too shocked to speak, but Zelda appears not to notice. She tells me where to bank money and how to pay the bills. She says that, as I will be the new manager, I can give myself a small pay increase.

"But only if there are enough takings. If not, you'll have to give yourself a pay cut instead."

I start to ask how the owner can justify this, but, before I can think of how to articulate what I want to say, Zelda goes. I watch my love walk away, her silhouette receding like a ghost, or a vapour trail, until it dissolves in the grey city morning.

I close the shop and sit in silence, forlorn. I've harboured thoughts of leaving, too. I've dreamt of somehow making a name for myself, then returning to claim Zelda. The only tangible part of this childish fantasy was Zelda. What will I dream of now that she's gone?

I sit with my head in my hands until, outside, life begins. The time has come, I decide, for me to stop sleeping during the day. I scribble some words on the bookshop's heavy duty, white bond, unwatermarked stationery, then go to the fourth floor, resignation letter in hand.

Zelda told me to leave notes in a box by the door, but I decide to knock. There's no answer. I knock again. Silence. I have nothing to lose but the object of my curiosity, so I take a deep breath, then turn the door handle. Unbidden, I enter the unlocked room.

There's nothing there.

The room is big enough for a person to live in, just. I could see the owner managing to fit in a small desk, a fold-up bed and, perhaps, a wardrobe. Not much else. There is a skylight, but when I try to open it, the mechanism is rusty and stiff. There is no indication that anyone has ever lived in here.

I sit on the floor of the dark, tiny room for hours until, outside, the sun is at its highest and more light creeps in. Slowly, I begin to work everything out.

There is no owner. There never has been.

After I've been sitting in the empty room for a whole day, I realise what, for all I know, Zelda guessed from the very start. Nobody owned The All Night Bookshop. The shop owned us.

At the stroke of midnight I go downstairs, unlock the door, and, while I wait for the first customer to arrive, put a note on the counter, inviting applications for a new assistant.

Silver Moon

Your names, old records, *Court and Spark, Dark Side of the Moon,*
A shop window welcome; open hands, new friends.
A wintery evening, nights drawing in. Warm glow:
Sisterwrite, Compendium, Silver Moon.

How you grew up reading nights to dawn.
Books you found only here, the then unknowns:
Audre Lorde, Nikki Giovanni, Toni Cade Bambara;
The Bluest Eye held up a haunting mirror, Pecola Breedlove.

Switched lights on; eyes wide open – *Sula, Corregidora*
You read and read with wonder: *We Are Everywhere:*
Writings About Lesbian Parents! Or *A Raisin in the Sun.*
Voices from Women's Liberation, Maya, Djuna, Zora,

The Spinster and Her Enemies! Or Lucille Clifton.
And by the silvery light of the bookshop you grew up
By the open door, standing alone, together,
Other readers as engrossed, browsing, basking –

The blessed benevolence, the sweet, sweet ambience
Of independent bookshops, remember Thins!
Look how you still love their names: Voltaire and Rousseau,
Grassroots, books gathering and honing your years:

Black and white striped spines, tiny irons, Viragos, Shebas,
The distinct spiral on the cover of your old *The Bell Jar*
Your skin's pages; your heart's ink, your brain's Word Power:
Jamaica Kincaid, Bessie Head, Claribel Alegría

Don't let them turn the lights out, dears.
Keep them safe, New Beacons, shining stars,
Look how you've aged with your beloved books, dear hearts.
Keep coming in, keep the bookshop door ajar.

Jackie Kay